CLASSIC LANDFORMS OF THE
SOUTH DEVON COAST

CLASSIC LANDFORMS OF THE

SOUTH DEVON COAST

DEREK MOTTERSHEAD

Edge Hill University College

Series editors
Rodney Castleden and Christopher Green

Published by the Geographical Association
in conjunction with the
British Geomorphological Research Group

THE GEOGRAPHICAL ASSOCIATION

THE BRITISH GEOMORPHOLOGICAL RESEARCH GROUP

PREFACE

Geomorphologists study landforms and the processes that create and modify them. The results of their work, published as they invariably are in specialist journals, usually remain inaccessible to the general public. We would like to put that right. Scattered across the landscapes of England and Wales there are many beautiful and striking landforms that delight the eye of the general public and are also visited by educational parties from schools, colleges and universities. Our aim in producing this series of guides is to make modern explanations of these classic landforms available to all, in a style and format that will be easy to use in the field. We hope that an informed understanding of the origins of the features will help the visitor to enjoy the landscape all the more.

Encouraged by the success of the first edition of the Classic Landform Guides we are pleased to introduce this new edition, enhanced by colour photographs, new illustrations and with the valuable addition of 1:50 000 map extracts by kind permission of the Education Team, Ordnance Survey. The relevant maps for the area covered in this booklet are the Ordnance Survey 1:50 000 Landranger sheets 192 and 202; please refer to the current Ordnance Survey Index for 1:25 000 availability.

Rodney Castleden *Roedean School, Brighton*
Christopher Green *Royal Holloway, University of London*

© the Geographical Association, 1981, 1997
As a benefit of membership, the Association allows its members
to reproduce material for their own internal school/departmental use,
provided that the copyright is held by the GA and that the user acknowledges
the source. This waiver does not apply to Ordnance Survey mapping, questions
about which should be referred to the Ordnance Survey.

ISBN 1 899085 37 8

This edition first published 1997

Published by the Geographical Association, Solly Street, Sheffield S1 4BF.
The views expressed in this publication are those of the authors and do not
necessarily represent those of the Geographical Association.

The Geographical Association is a registered charity no. 313129.

Cover photograph: Sunset over Prawle Point. *Photo:* FSC at Slapton Ley Field Centre
Frontispiece: South Hallsands, 1980. *Photo:* Derek Mottershead.

CONTENTS

Acknowledgements
The Geographical Association would like to thank the following organisations for permission to reproduce material in this publication: The Cookworthy Museum, Kingsbridge and the Field Studies Council at Slapton Ley Field Centre.
Mapping reproduced from Ordnance Survey
1:50 000 Landranger mapping with permission of
The Controller of The Stationery Office © Crown Copyright 82324M 09/96
Copy editing: Rose Pipes
Illustrations: Paul Coles
Series design concept: Quarto Design, Huddersfield
Design and typesetting: Armitage Typo/Graphics, Huddersfield
Printed and bound in Hong Kong by: Colorcraft Limited

INTRODUCTION

Coastlines are among the most dynamic geomorphological environments, and bear witness to many processes and episodes of landscape change. A coastline cuts a section across a land mass which may reveal the variety of geological materials of which the landscape is composed. This variety of materials, ranging from massive indurated rock to loose unconsolidated sediment, accounts in part for the variety of coastal landforms.

At the coast the erosional energy of the sea is brought to bear on the margin of the land. This is derived principally from two sources – waves and tides. Wave energy is the driving force behind almost every coastal process. Sea waves are caused by the wind blowing across the water surface, and their height is proportional to the strength of the wind and the length of the water surface (the **fetch**) across which it blows. Tidal energy is important in that it causes wave energy to be applied to all levels on the shore between high and low water. Thus wave processes sweep up and down throughout the tidal range daily.

Coastlines are in a continuous state of change, on a variety of timescales. The daily operation of the tidal cycle causes the hour to hour variation in tide level. The monthly tidal cycle produces variations in the tidal range from the maximum at springs to the minimum at neaps. The episodic occurrence of storms superimposes large and powerful waves upon these tide levels. Sea-level also varies over much longer timescales – the post-glacial rise in sea-level spanned several thousand years and terminated some 5000 years ago (Figure 1). Further back in time, during the Quaternary period, climatic changes caused major alterations in the processes which were modifying the landscape.

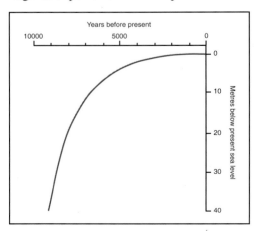

Figure 1: The Flandrian (post-glacial) rise in sea-level.

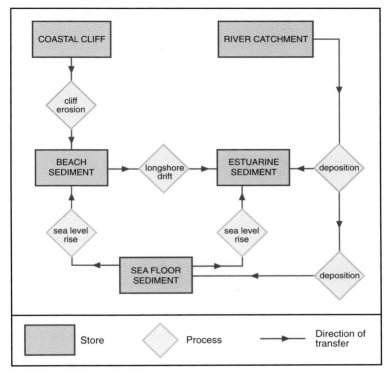

Figure 2: Pathways of sediment transfer in the coastal zone.

Rock materials are brought within reach of coastal processes in several ways. High cliffs may be rendered unstable by undercutting and rock material may fall directly to the shore below. The sediment load of rivers is delivered to the coast from inland river basins. Coarse sediment may be deposited directly at the coast in the form of gravel bars, whilst finer material may be carried further to be deposited as deltaic sediments or as offshore sea bed sediments. In the past, the rise in mean sea-level provided a further mechanism of sediment delivery to the coastal zone. As sea-level was rising, wave processes dredged sediment from the now submerged sea bed, and drove it shorewards. We can therefore regard the coastal zone as a repository (or **store**) of transitory sediments, which have been derived from a variety of sources (Figure 2).

The form of the coastline may be viewed as the result of the interaction between saline coastal waters on the one hand and rocks and sediments on the other. It represents a conflict between marine energy and terrestrial materials. The coast may respond at varying speeds to the application of marine forces: high cliffs of hard rock respond slowly to weathering and erosion over spans of many years, whereas in zones of abundant unconsolidated sediment coastal change may be very rapid indeed and substantial change may be evident even after a single storm.

Human activity may also have a significant impact on coastal processes. The coastal zone is the location of many human activities – habitation, port and harbour functions, fishing, recreation – and their outcome. As a consequence structures have been created in the coastal zone which themselves may become subject to coastal processes. Human activity may also have the effect of modifying coastal form or process, either deliberately or inadvertently, occasionally with disastrous consequences if the natural processes were not first fully understood.

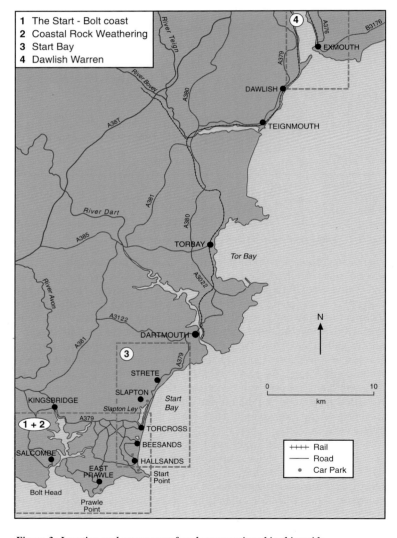

1 The Start - Bolt coast
2 Coastal Rock Weathering
3 Start Bay
4 Dawlish Warren

Figure 3: Location and access map for places mentioned in this guide.

8

Many of these principles and themes are illustrated by the South Devon coast (Figure 3). The effects of climatic and sea-level change on the broader timescale are here interwoven with contemporary geomorphological processes and the effects of human activity. Thus the Start-Bolt (Head) coast illustrates the effects of climate and sea-level change over the Quaternary timescale (Table 1). Contemporary rock weathering processes are also revealed here, in conjunction with the weathering of historic structures in the Salcombe estuary. The drastic consequences of human interference with natural processes are demonstrated at South Hallsands, and both that site and Dawlish Warren illustrate the rapidity of coastal change where mobile sediment is present.

Table 1: The geological periods, indicating those present at localities in this guide (see also Figure 4 overleaf).

Period (age in ma)	Oldest rock present	Formations material	Types of	Location
Quaternary[1] (including Flandrian)	2	Blown sand **Alluvium** Head Raised beach Sand Gravel	Loose sand Silt and clay sediments Gravelly earth	Salcombe estuary Slapton Ley Dawlish Warren and Exmouth estuary
Tertiary	65	none	none	none
Cretaceous	146	none	none	none
Jurassic	208	none	none	none
Triassic	245	none	none	none
Permian	290	Sandstone Breccia and conglomerate	Soft red sandstone Sandstone with pebbles	Dawlish Warren
Carboniferous	363	Quartz and mica schist Green schist	Hard grey lustrous schist Softer green schist	Start-Bolt coastline: Great Mattiscombe shore, Salcombe Castle, Limpyear Fortlet, sea wall North Sands Bay
Devonian	409	Meadfoot group Dartmouth slates	Slates and grits Purple and green slate	Start Bay: Strete, bed of Slapton Ley

Note: 1. Further sub-division of the latter part of the Quaternary is necessary in order to understand the following: **Flandrian:** the current temperate stage, spanning the last 10 000 years up to the present. **Devensian:** the last glacial stage, lasting from approximately 120 000 BP to 10 000 BP. **Ipswichian:** the temperate inter-glacial stage preceding the last glacial, and lasting from about 130 000 to 120 000 BP.

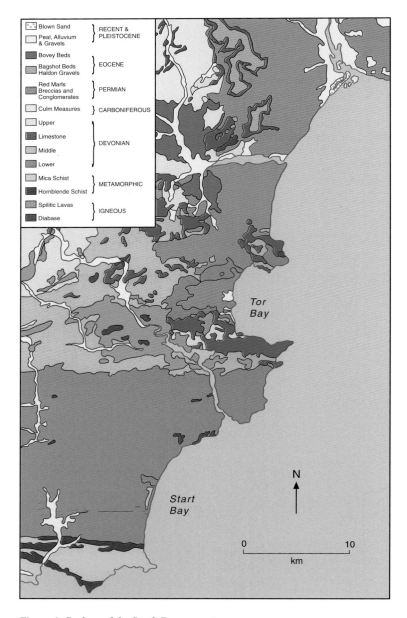

Legend:

Blown Sand	RECENT & PLEISTOCENE
Peat, Alluvium & Gravels	
Bovey Beds	EOCENE
Bagshot Beds Haldon Gravels	
Red Marls Breccias and Conglomerates	PERMIAN
Culm Measures	CARBONIFEROUS
Upper	
Limestone	DEVONIAN
Middle	
Lower	
Mica Schist	METAMORPHIC
Hornblende Schist	
Spilitic Lavas	IGNEOUS
Diabase	

Tor Bay

Start Bay

N

0   10
km

Figure 4: Geology of the South Devon coast.

THE START-BOLT COAST

The dramatic coastline between Start Point and Bolt Head is composed of **schists** formed some 300 million years ago in the Carboniferous period (Table 1 and Figure 4). The landscape is composed of several elements (Photo 1), reflecting a varied history of climatic and sea-level changes as well as a variety of **denudational processes** (Figure 5). The slope elements fall into two groups: elements 1-3 comprise the shore platforms, elements 4-6 comprise what we may regard as the coastal slopes. The two groups will be treated separately.

The shore platforms

An outstanding feature of the Start-Bolt (Head) coastline is the existence of bedrock platforms along the foreshore. In 1960, Orme recognised three platforms, distinguished by elevation, which form a rough staircase descending towards the sea, each platform separated from the next by a small vertical cliff. Orme designated these platforms as 24 foot (7.5m), 14 foot (4.5m) and post-Flandrian platforms, but such precise designations of elevations are inappropriate, and the interpretation of post-Flandrian age is misleading. We shall refer to them here as the high, middle and low platforms – terms which are sufficient to identify them but carry no implications of precise form or age.

Careful observation is required in order to identify the individual platforms, for the relations between them tend to be masked by a variety of complicating factors:

i The indentation of the coastline is mirrored by the **planform** of the platform. A particular platform will appear sometimes as a promontory, sometimes in a cove.

ii The platform will have a perceptible slope in a seaward direction; an individual platform will therefore appear at a different elevation according to whether it is a seaward or a landward fragment that is observed. This variation in height of an individual platform is the reason why it is unrealistic to use a single value of elevation as a label.

iii The rocks are severely dissected by the active erosion processes on this exposed coastline that the platforms are fragmented and it

Photo 1: Elements of the Start-Bolt (Head) coastline *(cp. Figure 5)*
Photo: FSC at Slapton Ley Field Studies Centre.

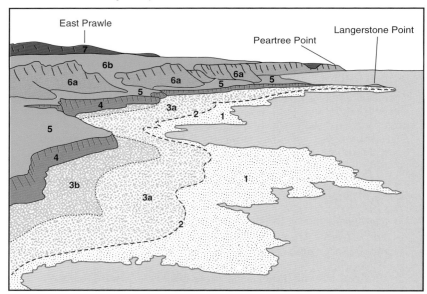

Figure 5: *Outline field sketch of the view eastwards from Prawle Point at low tide illustrating the major morphological elements of the landscape. After: Peter Keene.*
Key to the elements: 1. Rocky shore platform below HWM; 2. Break of slope (rather irregular); 3. Rocky shore platform (higher level) above HWM, within which can be distinguished, (a) bright green freshly weathered zone (patchy), (b) dull grey lichen covered zone; 4. Earth cliff up to 5m high; vertical slope exposing blocks and stones set in an earthy matrix (head); 5. Smoothly concave slopes extending seawards; 6. Craggy cliffs (a) up to 30m high formed of bedrock outcrop, (b) chutes extending down between the bedrock crags; 7. The plateau of the South Hams.

12

is difficult to correlate the fragments. The platforms are in places dissected by canyon-like gullies with vertical rock walls, representing former zones of penetration by deep **weathering**, from which the weathered material has been etched out by the sea. Occasionally it is possible to trace the canyons back to the cliff and detect the remaining deep weathered rock. Elsewhere indentations tens of metres in width have been cut out by the sea.

iv The structural complexity and brittleness of the bedrock itself has led to the development of rough-hewn and craggy outlines, often defined by joint planes exposed by the removal of jointed blocks. The relative scarcity of clear-cut features of marine **denudation** is a hindrance to interpretation.

v The extent to which the platforms have been exposed depends on how far the **head** which buries them has been stripped back. It is often the case that the head has been stripped back closer to the bedrock slope on the promontories, and the platforms tend to be more completely exposed there.

The distribution of and relationships between the platforms can best be observed at low tide, when they are most extensively displayed. Relationships are clearer on sunny days when the relief is picked out by patterns of light and shade. A good starting point is to identify the junction between the two platforms. The upper end of one platform is typically marked by a smoothly abraded notch which undercuts a vertical rock cliff 2-4m high, separating it from the next higher platform. Once such a feature has been identified it is then usually possible to identify which two of the three platforms are represented locally. Occasionally all three are present and visible at one locality. At Sharpers Cove (SX 785358) two can be seen at low tide. The footpath down the cliff leads on to a well marked platform fringing the cove above HWM at an elevation of +2 to +4m **OD** (Figure 6). At low tide, it can be seen to be separated by cliffs from a lower platform at an elevation of zero to -2m OD. Just as both platforms have a seaward gradient, so the notch at the base of the cliff varies in elevation along the length, rising as the lower platform penetrates inland.

Traces of a second cliff are also visible at Sharpers Cove. The platform above HWM is backed by a bedrock cliff adjacent to the descending footpath. This may be interpreted as the junction between the exposed platform and the next higher one which is not visible here since it remains buried by the slope deposits. The two visible platforms may therefore be identified as the middle and lower platforms. As a general guideline the middle/lower platform junction lies at a clearly higher elevation. The low platform is the most extensively exposed of the three; it largely occupies the inter-tidal elevations of the shore, and is partially occupied by beach sediment.

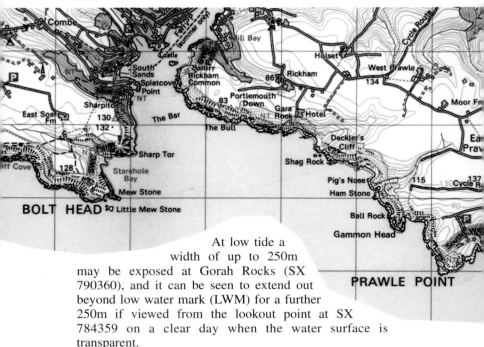

At low tide a width of up to 250m may be exposed at Gorah Rocks (SX 790360), and it can be seen to extend out beyond low water mark (LWM) for a further 250m if viewed from the lookout point at SX 784359 on a clear day when the water surface is transparent.

The middle platform commonly outcrops above HWM and forms the upper part of the foreshore. In many places it is overlain by slope deposits and forms the base of the head cliffs (Photo 2). Where it is distant from the direct action of the sea spray it has a conspicuous lichen cover. At Sharpers Cove, close to HWM, it forms a clear-cut platform; at Gorah Rocks it is obscured by beach sediment accumulated above HWM. At Harris' Beach (SX 805371) it is a well-developed plane surface extending down towards LWM.

Most of the upper platform remains buried and invisible and is exposed only in isolated fragments, where the slope deposits have been well trimmed back. Fragments of the high platform can be identified at Stinking Cove (SX 794365), on the promotories flanking Evator Cove (SX 798368) and at The Narrows (SX 818371). Malcombe Point, Woodcombe Sand (SX 796368), Great Mattiscombe Sand (SX 816369) (Photo 3) and Harris' Beach are good sites at which to observe the relationships between the platforms, especially at low tide.

Traces of beach sediment rest directly on the raised platforms, preserved under slope deposits. In many places the raised beach consists of well-sorted sand in a bed up to 30cm deep, but it is not always well represented; near Langerstone Point it is a mere smattering of flint pebbles in the base of the head deposits.

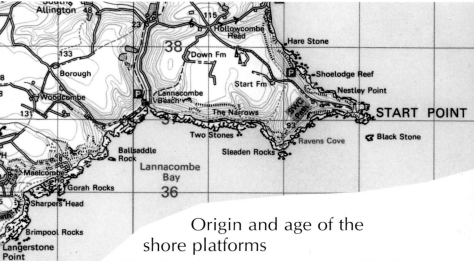

Origin and age of the shore platforms

The three shore platforms are of considerable geomorphological significance, each representing a major episode of marine erosion. Platform remnants only recently exhumed from beneath the head are seen to have smooth surfaces, suggesting that abrasion by beach sediment was responsible for their formation. They represent three phases when the sea-level was constant for long enough for platforms to develop. Assuming that the abrasion notch always developed up to mean high water spring tides (MHWST) and that past tidal ranges were similar to those of today, then the sea-levels responsible for the formation of the platforms would have been approximately 7m, 4m and 0m above present sea-level.

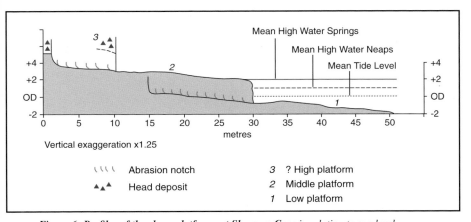

Figure 6: Profiles of the shore platforms at Sharpers Cove in relation to sea-level.

Photo 2: Elongated clasts of schist protude from the head cliff at Sharpers Head.
Their disposition reveals the near-horizontal bedding, and the downslope of the long axes. Photo: FSC at Slapton Ley Field Centre.

Photo 3: Great Mattiscombe Sand.
In the centre is the prominent degraded cliff formed in the head, and up to 20m high. It overlies a section of the middle rock platform, which is also represented by the isolated stack at the water line. The concave slope of the surface formed by the head rises towards tors at the crest of the slope in the background. Photo: FSC at Slapton Ley Field Centre.

The ages of the platforms pose a considerable problem. The beach sediments contain no fossils or other material that is datable. Even if they did, there may have been a considerable lag in between platform formation and beach deposition. Nevertheless, it seems likely that their ages increase upwards. The low platform, currently washed and abraded by the sea, is almost certainly not a product of present marine erosion. The formation of a 500m wide platform during the last 50 000 years implies a rate of notch recession of 0.1m per year, but the current rate of notch recession seems to be less than 1 per cent of this value. It therefore seems most likely that the low platform was formed during a period of sea-level similar to the present, but at some time in the distant past. The present sea-level is thus reoccupying an ancient shore platform.

The coastal slopes

The earth cliffs varying in height from 2m to 20m, which overlook the shore platform, offer excellent viewing opportunities to observe the material which forms the coastal slopes. Exposed throughout the cliff (except sometimes at their base) is an unconsolidated sediment comprising blocks and stones set in an earthy matrix (ie. head). It is this material which forms the earth cliff shown in Figure 5. It has a number of readily observable characteristics, as follows:

i   The sediment is unsorted in that it may contain particles ranging from boulders right down the scale to silt and clay.

ii The coarse stones are angular in shape and elongated in form, as determined by cleavage planes.

iii The stones are oriented with their long axes pointing downslope. Since many are elongated in form they tend to project from the earth cliffs.

iv The material comprising the sediment is entirely locally derived **schist** and quartz; furthermore the variety of schist present in the cliff reflects that exposed in the underlying bedrock of the platform. Only near a junction in outcrops are the two types of schist (grey quartz-mica schist and green hornblende-chlorite schist) present together in the cliff.

v   Occasionally a crude impression of stratification is visible within the sediments forming the cliffs.

These characteristics indicate that the sediment has only travelled a short distance before being emplaced in its present position, and also that the transportation involved little if any selective sorting. Additionally, no rounding of the **clasts** was effected during transport. Such sediments are characteristic of mass movement down slope in a **periglacial** environment, by the process of gelifluction. This involves alternate heaving and settling of soil on the slope during freezing and thawing, and also the creep of the soil saturated by the water during thawing. Thus the layers of soil, often in the form of terraces, are

17

transferred downslope, stripping the regolith (mantle of weathered rock) from the upper part of the slope and re-depositing it lower down. In general, the further the material was transported the finer it became. It is exposed close to the bedrock cliff from which it is derived at Sharpers Cove, and clasts up to 1m long can be observed there. At localities distant from the bedrock slope, eg. Langerstone Point, the largest fragments are gravel-sized.

The extent to which the pre-existing landscape was modified by this process can be gauged by considering the depth and distribution of the slope deposits. Locally the land surface has been raised by accumulation of up to 20m of this sediment. The rock cliffs and slopes above them would have been lowered by the stripping of the former weathered mantle. The relief in the landscape from divide to valley floor would have been significantly higher prior to periglaciation. The fact that the coastal slopes are terminated by cliffs indicates that the slope deposits formerly extended further seaward. The slope material doubtless mantled the rock platforms much more extensively, indicating that deposition took place during times of lower sea-level. Subsequently a rise in sea-level has trimmed the slope deposits back as far as the present position of the earth cliffs. Where protected by an underlying promontory of bedrock, as at Langerstone Point, the slope deposits extend seawards for some 300m. Where marine erosion has penetrated close to the bedrock cliff, as at Sharpers Cove, the slope deposits have been trimmed right back.

The slope deposits are best considered in relation to the crags which form the rocky cliffs overlooking them. These crags would have been initially exposed by the stripping of the overlying weathered mantle. Once exposed to the atmosphere under the periglacial conditions of the time the rock outcrops would have been attacked by frost weathering exploiting the many joints and fractures. Angular blocks of rock were riven from these crags and now bestrew the slopes beneath them. The exposed crags are **tors**, and the spreads of angular rock debris are **blockfields**. That the weathering processes responsible for their formation are no longer active is indicated by the lack of freshness of the features. The crags are often encrusted with lichens and the blockfields overgrown by scrubby vegetation.

The coastal slopes are thus a legacy of past periglacial conditions and display fossilised landforms that were created by processes active at least 10 000 years ago (Photo 4).

Access

See page 20 for information on access to this area.

The geomorphological evolution of the coast

It is now appropriate to consider the broad sequence of events responsible for shaping this section of the coastline (Figure 7). The oldest event of which evidence remains in the landscape is that of

Photo 4: The typical Bolt-Start coastal landscape.
Tors overlook smooth concave slopes terminating in earth cliffs. Two shore platforms
are visible both in the foreground and middle distance. Photo: Derek Mottershead.

deep weathering of the land surface. Deeply penetrated along the lines of weakness, the rotted bedrock may represent a very prolonged period of weathering. The oldest landforms present on this coastline are the shore platforms, eroded across the bedrock by wave action at different periods in the past when the sea was at its present level or higher. It is implicit in this that there exists an ancient cliff-line at the foot of the coastal slope, but it is not directly observable because of its burial beneath the more recent slope deposits.

Preliminary measurements of notch recession indicate a rate of about 0.5mm per year. At this rate the formation of a platform 500m in width would take a million years. It is clear therefore that the three shore platforms represent long periods when the sea was stable. As the sea receded from the ancient platforms, scattered patches of beach sediment were left stranded upon them.

The next significant change was the phase of periglacial activity which stripped the mantle of previously weathered rock and moved it downslope to form the shore deposits. These sediments flowed downslope and out across the ancient cliff-line to the rock platforms, burying them and the beach sediments resting upon them. At the same time the serrated rock outcrops emerged to form tors and subsequently the blockfield and scree deposits. Sea-level was lower than at present, enabling the slope deposits to extend further seawards than they do now.

With the post-glacial rise in sea-level the coastline was trimmed back yet again. The unconsolidated head cliffs yielded readily to marine denudation and have been stripped back to a position where they are largely protected from marine attack by underlying bastions of raised platforms. The low platform currently forms the inter-tidal zone and is being freshened up and trimmed by beach sediment under wave action, leading to the formation of smooth, fresh abrasion notches.

The raised platforms now exposed to weathering are being lowered very rapidly, particularly in the spray zone adjacent to HWM. The progressive effects of coastal weathering on the platform surface, following its exhumation from beneath the head, is amply demonstrated towards the western side of Great Mattiscombe shore (SX 815369). Here the quartz/mica schist of the middle platform has a smooth rounded surface close to the base of the slope deposits from beneath which it has recently been revealed. Traced seawards its surface becomes progressively more serrated due to differential weathering and at the seaward edge of the raised platform it has a relief of 30cm and more.

The present coastal landscape is an expression of a long and complex history of denudation, encompassing changes of great magnitude in climatic conditions and **subaerial** processes, as well as large fluctuations in the level of the sea.

Access

The Start-Bolt coast can be approached on foot at many points. The closest access for vehicular transport is at four parking sites:

- Prawle Point (SX 774354) – this is a National Trust car park (no fee required – but you are asked to make a contribution to the Trust).
- East Prawle village (SX 783359) – approach by a lane due south from East Prawle village green; turn left at SX 779359.
- Lannacombe Beach car park (SX 802372) – offers direct access to Lannacombe Beach.
- Start Point car park (SX 821375) – parking fee required.

The South West Coast Path follows the top of the cliffs along the entire stretch of this coastline, offering fine views of the coastal landforms as a whole. At low tide it is possible to traverse the length of the shore from Copstone Cove (SX 774352) to Peartree Cove (SX 818368).

The shore platform between Sharpers Cove and Langerstone Point is readily accessible from the low-level coastal path. There is a network of paths around Prawle Point, though care must be taken on clifftops.

There is ready access to the shore at Copstone Cove, Landing Cove, Langerstone Point, Sharpers Cove, Horseley Cove, Woodcombe Sand, Lannacombe Beach and Great Mattiscombe Sand. At any state

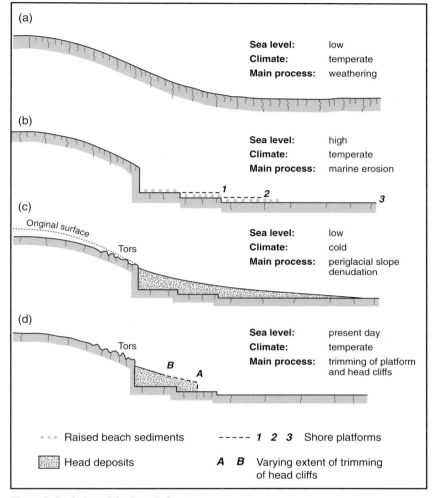

Figure 7: Evolution of the Start-Bolt coast.
Indicating the changing climatic and sea-level conditions, and the sequence of the geomorphological events: (a) early and pre Quaternary, (b) Ipswichian and early interglacials, (c) Devensian, and (d) Flandrian.

of the tide some degree of exploration along the shoreline is possible at all these points. On a rising tide, however, certain sections of the shoreline become impassable, notably in the vicinity of Ballsaddle Rock (SX 797365), The Narrows (SX 818371) and Limpet Cove (SX 812369). Escape is possible at several points by scrambling along rough paths up the face of the head cliffs, although this is not recommended for large school parties.

COASTAL ROCK WEATHERING

The coastal zone creates a distinctive weathering environment in which bedrock may come into contact with saline marine water. Seawater comprises a number of salts in solution (Table 2), of which the most abundant is sodium chloride (NaCl), and is thus a more effective agent of weathering than pure or rain water.

Certain rocks, by virtue of the minerals which compose them, react

Table 2: Salts crystallising from seawater.

Salt	g.kg-1
NaCl	27.21
MgCl2	3.81
MgSO4	1.66
CaSO4	1.26
K2SO4	0.86
CaCO3	0.12
MgBr2	0.08

strongly and weather rapidly in the marine environment. Green schist, which outcrops abundantly in this area, is one such rock. It is composed largely of minerals such as hornblende, epidote and chlorite whose internal crystalline structure is only rather weakly bonded. The effects of rapid weathering of this distinctive rock are locally displayed in a variety of contexts.

Along the shoreline

In the freshly weathered zone of the shore platforms (Photos 1 and 4, Figure 5; zone 3a), human activity has created situations in which the rapid weathering of coastal green schist has manifested itself. First, at Sharpers Cove (SX 785358), the remains of an iron stanchion sit embedded in a fillet of cement which stands proud of the green schist surface, into which it would originally have been inset. Second, particularly near Dutch End (SX 785356) and at Sharpers Cove, small patches of oil thrown up on the foreshore have preserved the rock beneath, whilst the surrounding rock has continued to be lowered by weathering. Thus oil-capped pedestals, congruent in planform with the oil patch and up to 11mm high, have begun to emerge from the surrounding lowering surface. Third, at Sharpers Cove, grease employed in some erosion measurement experiments initiated in 1980 has seeped into the rock, sealing and binding it, and leading to the emergence of visible pedestals in as little as five years. These experiments have revealed a mean rate of weathering of the green schist surface in this locality of 0.62mm a^{-1} over a period of seven years.

Photo 5: Oil capped weathering pedestal.
The relief of the pedestal is highlighted by its shadow and the scale indicated by a ten pence coin. Photo: Derek Mottershead.

Photo 6: Pedestals formed by oil spills.
The planform of the pedestal is congruent with the spill. The near pedestal is 11mm high, the rear one 3-4mm. The penknife measures 90mm in length.
Photo: Derek Mottershead.

The oil-capped pedestals (Photos 5 and 6) can be grouped into those with a continuous cap of oil, those on which the oil has begun to fray back from the margins, and those on which the oil has thinned and become patchy. Measurements have shown that the mean height of these three groups of pedestals increases in the order continuous > frayed > patchy, implying that these represent an evolutionary sequence as the oil gradually weathers away. This would suggest that when the oil has weathered completely away, the underlying pedestal loses its protection and is then destroyed. It is likely that some small stumps of rock represent the remains of former pedestals. The age of these groups, and thus the duration of oil on this exposed rocky shore, can be estimated by reference to the observed weathering rate of 0.62mm a^{-1}. Thus it appears that oil may persist for a maximum of 5-11 years without visible alteration. More commonly, shrinkage of the oil patches begins after 1-3 years, and thinning after 2-5 years, varying apparently with the thickness and type of oil. The highest oil-bearing pedestals have ages of 17-18 years, representing the maximum durability of oil on this exposed rocky shore.

The pedestals observed in the original study, carried out in 1979, have now disappeared, but have been replaced by new ones, supporting the interpretation of eventual pedestal decay. It also implies that there is a continuing supply of oil patches thrown up on the foreshore.

The coastal slopes

Many of the craggy outcrops which overlook the coastline (Figures 5 and 6) are formed of green schist, and these also bear evidence of recent fresh weathering. The view northward from the shore adjacent to The Island (SX 772350) reveals a high proportion of pale green, freshly weathered rock on these outcrops (Mottershead and Pye, 1994). Closer inspection shows that these fresh rock surfaces lie within small caverns inset into the rock outcrop (Photo 7). The fresh weathered surfaces contrast strongly with the grey lichen-covered older rock surfaces fronting the rock outcrops. These caverns are of the order of 2m high, 3m wide and 1.4m deep. They are characterised by overhanging and lateral visors behind which their internal dimensions open out. There is commonly a collection of granular sediment, composed mainly of sand- and silt-sized particles, on ledges within the caverns and on the floors. This is debris which has resulted from the breakdown of the rock by granular disintegration. The internal form of the caverns implies that the internal walls recede laterally backwards and vertically upwards. The outer surface of the rock outcrops is often stained brown, with an accumulation of rock minerals. This appears to have an armouring effect on the rock surface, which, once breached, then leads to more rapid recession of the rock behind. This is visible in its early stages on a steep rock outcrop to the right of the path leading from Copstone

Photo 7: A weathering cavern on the coastal slope.
The interior walls have a fresh appearance. Within the cavern, recessed beneath the overhang, some secondary hollows have developed. A metre rule provides scale. Photo: Derek Mottershead.

Cove (SX 774352) up towards the coastguard signal station (SX 773351). Here the brown-stained patina is still fresh, and is punctured at several points at which thimble-sized depressions have begun to indent the rock surface, opening out laterally as they penetrate.

On dated historic structures

Historic structures offer the possibility of studying the effects of rock weathering over known periods of time. Furthermore, if the structures are located in a similar position and thus share a similar weathering environment, this offers the opportunity to conduct a controlled scientific experiment on the effects of weathering. In the Salcombe estuary a number of structures, all composed of similar green schist, are located just above HWM. The major ones are Salcombe Castle (SX 734381), originally built in 1544 and partially reconstructed in 1644 (Photo 8); Limpyear Fortlet (SX 736384), built in 1802; and the sea wall at North Sands Bay (SX 731382), initially built in 1858 and repaired several times over the next 25 years (Mottershead, 1997). These structures display several weathering forms, and permit the identification of the rate of weathering over known periods of historic time.

Photo 8: Salcombe Castle, a general view.
The circular wall, exposed to the open sea, exhibits the greatest effects of weathering.
The tall narrow bastion at the northern end has slates interleaved with green schist
which reveal the original wall line, and thus the depth of weathering of the green schist
may be measured. Photo: Derek Mottershead.

Observation of rock weathering must be related to the form of the
original surface of the rock or wall. This is readily identifiable in the
case where individual pits indent a recognisable initial surface.
Elsewhere, the line of the initial surface must be inferred from less
direct evidence such as an original surface on an adjacent stone, or a
vein of resistant or unweathered quartz standing out from the green
schist courses. Rock weathering can be identified in a variety of forms
(Photo 9). Individual pits may indent the rock surface, in places
multiplying to form a honeycomb network. More extensive
weathering may take the form of general recession of the whole rock
face. The most extreme form of weathering takes the form known as
boxwork (see Photos 9 and 10), in which the central core has been
weathered out from a rock whose margins have been reinforced by
hardening due to migration into them of minerals from adjacent
materials (often mortar in the case of rocks in built walls).

The depth of weathering, and the distribution of the different forms
are a function of the disparate ages of the structures, and within each
one, differences in the degree of exposure to agents of weathering.
Thus individual pits, and some honeycomb and general recession are
visible at North Sands Bay (SX 731383), general recession is more
common at Limpyear Fortlet, and boxwork is abundant on the oldest
structure of Salcombe Castle.

Photo 9: Various forms of weathering demonstrated by the parapet stones on North Sands Bay retaining wall.
The stone at left shows limited isolated pitting; the central stone has a completely recessed surface; the stone at right shows both honeycomb and a large weathering pit (tafone) in its lower part. Photo: Derek Mottershead.

Photo 10: Boxwork developed on the section of the seaward side of a wall at Salcombe Castle.
Individual building stones are completely hollowed by weathering within the armoured shell which forms their outline. Photo: Derek Mottershead.

Field observations show that the retaining wall at North Sands Bay possesses maximum depths of weathering (of a mean of ten adjacent stones) of around 88mm, Limpyear Fortlet around 120mm and Salcombe Castle 250mm. In general these observations of the depth of weathering indicate that a maximum rate of around 0.6mm a^{-1} is applicable to all three structures up to a timespan of 350 years.

Within each structure the influence of local factors can be detected. On the parapet stones, which are readily observed from both sides of North Sands Bay wall, the weathering is more pronounced on the exposed seaward side than on the sheltered landward side. Furthermore, a greater extent and intensity of weathering is evident in a traverse from south-west to north-east commensurate with the greater exposure of that end of the wall, to sea waves arriving onshore from a wider arc of exposure to the mouth of the estuary. These variations manifest themselves both in depth of weathering observed and in the proportion of stones showing weathering forms. Exposure to marine agents, spray and salt, thus appears to be a controlling factor.

At Salcombe Castle, the 350-year-old circular wall at the south end of the structure shows the influence of aspect. The depth of weathering is at its greatest on the section of wall most exposed to sea waves and winds, diminishing around to the more sheltered side. The 450-year-old straight wall facing the land cliff is weathered to a lesser depth and many original stone surfaces are still visible. At the northern end of the structure, a two-faced bastion shows various degrees of weathering of the two faces, of which the north-facing one never receives direct sunlight, is less immediately exposed to salt spray, and is significantly less deeply weathered.

These examples demonstrate that such structures can be used to control the depth (and therefore the rate) of weathering. Factors such as aspect, and thereby direct exposure to solar radiation and the input of salt via spray or dry aerosol are shown to be direct influences. The actual mechanism of coastal weathering of green schist is shown by Mottershead and Pye (1994) to be chemical corrosion at the boundaries of the grains which form the rocks. This causes them to detach from each other, thereby disintegrating the rock. The corrosion is most likely to be caused by the individual elements in the marine salts.

Access

The retaining wall at North Sands Bay is accessible at all states of the tide.

Salcombe Castle is accessible at low tide only, although there is an escape route up the cliffs just north by a small marina (it is difficult, however, to find this route in the downward direction). Some care needs to be taken in scrambling around the base of the castle walls.

Limpyear Fortlet is accessible by permission through the grounds of the house named 'Woodville' on Cliff Road, or by boat.

START BAY

The coastline between Start Point (SX 830370) and Pilchard Cove (SX 844465) offers a range of interesting landforms all related to the movement of shingle round Start Bay, both under present conditions and in the past. The Start Bay coast cuts across the dissected plateau landscape of the South Hams. Much of the central section of the coast is formed by the slates of the Meadfoot series of Lower Devonian age which carry plateau surfaces at around +90m OD. The plateau surface rises to 140m to the north at Strete, where the Dartmouth Slates outcrop, and to a similar elevation at the south where the Start Schists occur (Figure 4). The plateau is dissected by a series of valleys which drain towards Start Bay, creating a coastline of alternating resistant rocky headlands and indented valley mouths.

The most significant landform is the continuous barrier of shingle which extends for a distance of 9km throughout the length of this coast (Figure 8). For approximately half of its length the shingle barrier is built against the foot the cliffs, but where these are cut by the valleys the drainage has been impounded. This has resulted in the formation of lakes of which Slapton Ley is the outstanding example. A smaller lake exists at Beesands whilst a former one at North Hallsands has been filled in by sedimentation.

Slapton Sands

The longest section of the barrier which is detached from the bedrock terrain is the 3.5km length of Slapton Sands, extending from Torcross to Strete Gate. It is the local equivalent of the much longer shingle structure of Chesil Beach (see Brunsden and Goudie, 1997). The name Slapton Sands is really a misnomer, for the beach is predominantly a shingle structure; it is also incorrectly identified on Ordnance Survey maps as a 'Raised beach'.

The planform of Slapton Sands is slightly concave, following the curve of Start Bay. The shingle ridge is 110m broad at the northern end and narrows to 83m at Torcross. Its crest, about 8m above HWM at Pilchard Cove, declines to 5.5m at Torcross. It is important to appreciate, however, that the true scale of the barrier is greater than that exposed above HWM. At the central car park (SX 829442) the crest is about +6m OD and the exposed width about 136m from MHWST to lake shore, but the total depth of shingle is 11m, and it rests on marine muds whose surface lies at about -5m OD. The total width of the shingle bank is 450m, its cross-section tapering both

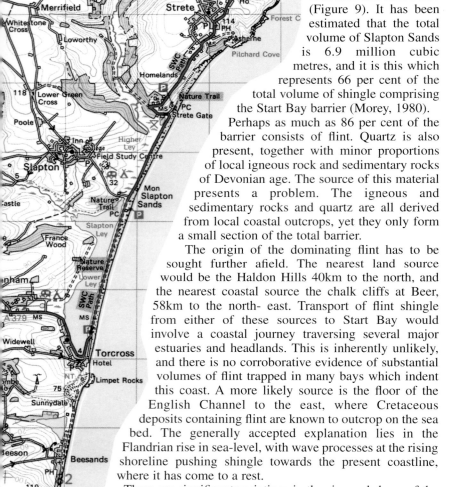

seawards and landwards (Figure 9). It has been estimated that the total volume of Slapton Sands is 6.9 million cubic metres, and it is this which represents 66 per cent of the total volume of shingle comprising the Start Bay barrier (Morey, 1980).

Perhaps as much as 86 per cent of the barrier consists of flint. Quartz is also present, together with minor proportions of local igneous rock and sedimentary rocks of Devonian age. The source of this material presents a problem. The igneous and sedimentary rocks and quartz are all derived from local coastal outcrops, yet they only form a small section of the total barrier.

The origin of the dominating flint has to be sought further afield. The nearest land source would be the Haldon Hills 40km to the north, and the nearest coastal source the chalk cliffs at Beer, 58km to the north-east. Transport of flint shingle from either of these sources to Start Bay would involve a coastal journey traversing several major estuaries and headlands. This is inherently unlikely, and there is no corroborative evidence of substantial volumes of flint trapped in many bays which indent this coast. A more likely source is the floor of the English Channel to the east, where Cretaceous deposits containing flint are known to outcrop on the sea bed. The generally accepted explanation lies in the Flandrian rise in sea-level, with wave processes at the rising shoreline pushing shingle towards the present coastline, where it has come to a rest.

There are significant variations in the size and shape of the shingle present. There is a marked grading of size, coarser to finer from north to south, but little significant variation from crest to sea. These observations suggest that a long-term sorting process is at work along the shore, but that short-term processes do not affect the vertical distribution of pebble size. Borehole samples indicate that shingle at and near the surface is well rounded whilst that at depth is more angular and a little weathered. This pattern is entirely consistent with the reworking of the surface layers by wave action following the emplacement of the barrier.

A study by Job (1993) indicates that the barrier beach is now wider towards its northern end at Strete, though according to map evidence the

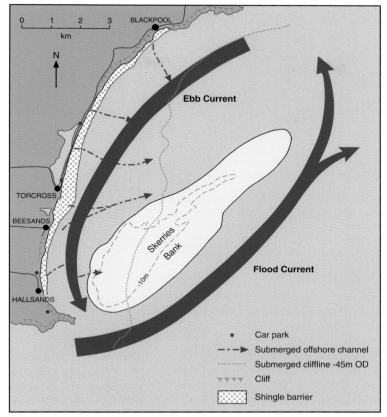

Figure 8: Geomorphological features of Start Bay.
The strong ebb current running southwards close inshore sweeps the sea bed clear of sediment and helps prevent beach replenishment by inshore movement of sediment from the Skerries Bank. The former low level of the sea is indicated by the drowned landscape on the floor of the bay, comprising submerged river channels and a submerged cliff-line at -45m OD. After: Hails, 1975.

converse appeared to be the case in the nineteenth century. Photographic and survey evidence suggests that in recent decades there has been a general shift of beach sediment in a northward direction. If this were a permanent trend the integrity of the barrier, which has existed for some 3000 years, would have been destroyed by now. This implies the existence of a longer-term cyclic fluctuation whereby sediment migrates alternately northwards and southwards alongshore, whilst maintaining the barrier form.

Job also shows the effect of short-term (day-to-day) variations in beach profile caused by storm waves from various directions, as a result of which beach sediment is either driven up or combed down the beach face, or exchanged with the nearshore zone. In the short-term, there appears to be no significant drift of sediment alongshore.

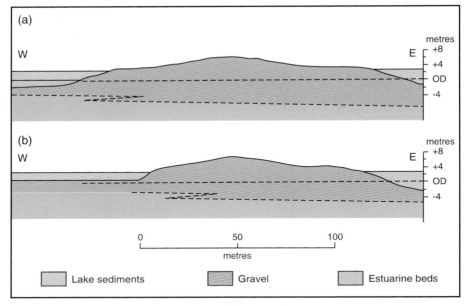

Figure 9: Cross-sections of the shingle barrier at Slapton and Torcross. After: Morey 1980.

Table 3 summarises the wave and beach conditions associated with different wave and wind types. Typical inter-tidal beach gradients range from 7° (flat) to 10° (steep) on the coarse shingle at Torcross, with lower values of 6° (flat) to 8° (steep) on the sandy beach at Strete.

Slapton Ley

The landward movement of the shingle barrier (Photo 11) has impounded the drainage of three small rivers to form a lake, Slapton Ley. This lake must be considered as an integral part of the coastal landscape because of its close relationship with the barrier: it also provides evidence of the barrier's age. Slapton Ley consists of two small basins linked by a narrow channel at Slapton Bridge (SX 828444). The smaller Higher Ley has almost entirely been colonised by reedswamp and carr, whilst Lower Ley has a considerable extent of open water, 0.77 sq km in area. Water drainage off the nearby land passes through the Ley before entering the sea through a culvert at Torcross.

The floor of the lake shelves gently from the margin down to a flat floor at about 2m below water level: a few small areas exceed about 2.5m in depth. At the landward side the lake basin is cut into and floored by slate gravel, whilst the seaward margin is formed by marine beach gravel of the barrier. The middle part of the lake bed is

Table 3: Wave and beach characteristics associated with different wind types in Start Bay.

Wind	Wave type	Action	Berm	Shingle movement	Inter-tidal profile
offshore	low, surging	constructive	present	onshore	steep
easterly, moderate, onshore	plunging	destructive	absent	offshore	flat
south, southeast, gales	steep, plunging	destructive	absent	offshore	flat
east, northeast, gales	alongshore	constructive	present	onshore	steep

Source: summarised from Job, 1993.

underlain either by an accumulation of peat, or beach gravel which has been thrown over the crest of the barrier by storms (called a washover fan) (Figure 10). Overlying all of these sediments is a clayey mud which is currently accumulating on the lake bed.

The history of the lake basin can be demonstrated by a study of the layers of sediment which have accumulated in it (Figure 11). At the base are marine sediments containing the shells of estuarine molluscs *(Hydrobia ventrosa, Abra tenuis)*. At the time these sediments were

Photo 11: Slapton shingle barrier, *curving away to the north of Start Bay and impounding the freshwater lagoon of Slapton Ley. Torcross Village can be seen in the foreground. Photo: Derek Mottershead.*

33

laid down the sea would have had access to the area of the Ley, although it would not have been a completely exposed coastline. Overlying these sediments is a substantial body of peat which accumulated on land under ill-drained conditions. The formation of peat therefore indicates that the site of the Ley was closed off from the direct influence of the sea, and yet was a land surface prior to the formation of the lake. The base of the peat has been radiocarbon dated as 2900 years old, and its surface at 1800 years old. These dates are valuable markers in the history of both the barrier and the lake. They provide the following information:

i   the shingle barrier was in place and complete at least 3000 years ago;

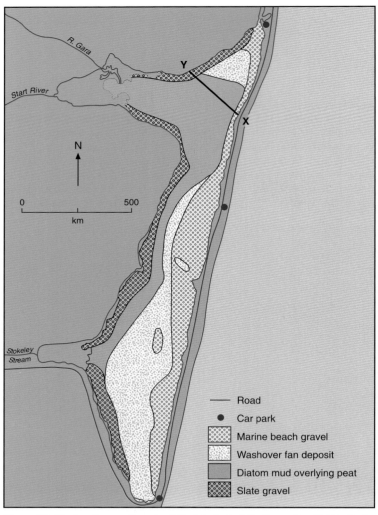

Figure 10: Slapton Ley - sediments of the lake bed of the Lower Ley (X-Y indicates the line of the cross-section shown in Figure 11). After: Morey 1976.

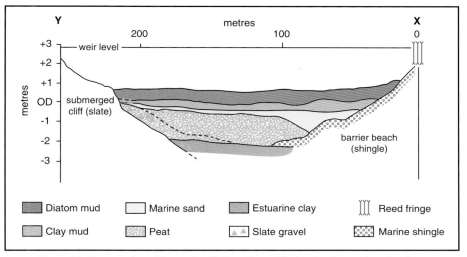

Y | metres | X
+3 — weir level
+2
OD — submerged cliff (slate)
-1
-2 — barrier beach (shingle)
-3

200   100   0

- ▨ Diatom mud
- ☐ Marine sand
- ▨ Estuarine clay
- Ⅲ Reed fringe
- ▨ Clay mud
- ▨ Peat
- ▲△ Slate gravel
- ▨ Marine shingle

Figure 11: Cross-section of Lower Ley (X-Y on Figure 10) showing the stratigraphy of the lake sediments. After: Morey, 1976.

ii   the phase of peat accumulation lasted for 1100 years;

iii   the lake itself and the sediments overlying the peat have formed within the past 1800 years.

The peat is in turn overlain by a thin layer of marine sand containing shell fragments at an elevation slightly below OD. This layer represents an episode, probably shortlived, in which the sea breached the shingle barrier. This sand is overlain by brown and black clay and mud (rich in small plants called **diatoms**) which have accumulated on the lake floor. The sediments composing these layers were introduced to the Ley by surface streams and when deposited formed an impervious seal against the shingle barrier. Only when this had taken place was the leakage of drainage water outwards through the barrier prevented and the waters impounded to form the lake. Slapton Ley, a prominent feature in the landscape, is therefore a recent feature, probably not older than 1500 years. Yet it is also a very temporary feature. Already the Higher Ley is virtually full of sediment and the Lower Ley has been reduced in area by substantial areas of deltaic sediments where streams enter.

The lake level has been raised slightly by the construction of a culvert to replace the natural drainage outlet at Torcross. This took place initially in 1856 when the road along the barrier (now the A379) was turnpiked. Since its original construction the weir has been raised at least once, thereby maintaining the level of water in the Slapton Ley at the artificially high level of +2.65m OD.

Heathwaite (1993) has demonstrated the effects of land use changes in the surrounding catchments by analysing the most recent sediment collecting on the bed of the Ley. Since 1945 agricultural activity in the area has become more intensive: grassland has been ploughed up, applications of nitrogen and phosphorus fertilisers have increased, and the density of animal stocks has increased. These changes have increased erosion from the land surface of sediment and soil minerals. Thus the rate of sedimentation in the Ley increased from 2mm a^{-1} in the 1930s to 10mm a^{-1} by the 1960s, an increase which introduced substantial volumes of silica and other common soil elements (such as aluminium and potassium) into the lake sediments. At the same time, the influx of phosphorus and nitrogen have modified the status of the lake from **eutrophic** to **hypertrophic**, resulting in greater organic productivity and an increased susceptibility to substantial **algal blooms.**

Torcross: Coastal processes and sea defences

The coast at Torcross provides an illustration of the activity of coastal processes and of the way in which human settlement in the coastal zone may be hazardous. Torcross is built on the southernmost section of Slapton Sands. It is tucked up against the northern flank of the ridge which forms the rocky sea cliff of Limpet Rocks (SX 824417), breaking the smooth sweep of the barrier. At the top of the beach is the Torcross Hotel, plus a row of cottages and other properties. Prior to the construction of the present sea defences a track ran along the front of the properties which was itself protected by a sea wall built about 1944.

Since that date there have been several instances of damages by storm waves, but none so serious as that which occurred between 30 December 1978 and 5 January 1979. A period of high spring tides was made more hazardous by the occurrence of strong easterly gales which had the effect of driving large waves estimated at 5.5m in amplitude directly onshore. Breaking waves threw water and shingle above roof level and properties were inundated as water gushed down alleys between them, causing considerable damage. This event prompted the consideration of flood hazard in the locality and led to the construction of the present sea defences.

As an initial step in identifying the nature and degree of hazard expected, tidal levels may be compared to the elevation of the adjacent coast. Tidal levels are as follows:

Once in 100 years tide level	+3.15m OD
Highest Astronomical Tide (HAT)	+2.85m OD
Mean High Water Spring Tides	+2.20m OD
Mean High Water Neap Tides	+1.00m OD

These compare with the level of the ridge crest which varies locally between +4.9 and +6.4m OD. It is clear from the height difference that a high tide level alone is not sufficient to overtop the barrier. What caused the 1978-79 storm damage was the breaking of the high waves which themselves raised the water level.

Comparison of high- and low-water marks on Ordnance Survey maps of 1908 and 1953 reveals that although HWM remained constant, LWM moved landward by about 22m during this period. This encroachment has caused the gradient of the beach to steepen from 1:15 to about 1:5, and photographic evidence (Job, 1993) suggests that the width of the beach at low water shortened from 100m to 50m between the 1930s and the 1980s, this in turn enabled large waves to move further inshore before breaking. Torcross village became more vulnerable to wave damage. The preventative works involved the construction of a new sea wall throughout the length of the exposed properties. Specific features of the new wall are as follows:

i   large boulders (rip-rap) cemented into the sloping lower face of the walls (their irregular surface dissipates the energy of breaking waves);

ii the curved undercut profile of the top of the wall (this is a wave return wall and is designed to deflect water away from the properties).

Beesands village south of Torcross, similarly affected by beach narrowing, has also recently been protected by substantial defences.

South Hallsands

The ruined village of South Hallsands lies at the foot of the Start promontory. The remains of former dwellings perch on a discontinuous rock shelf representing the remnants of a once-continuous rock platform whose surface stands at +6 to +8m OD sloping seawards across its width of up to 20m. It is separated by vertical cliffs (6-8m high) from a lower rock platform, currently washed by the sea, whose upper limit is marked by a notch at about zero OD on the promontories, but rising to higher elevations (+1m) up the ravines which cut into the higher platform.

Spectacular marine erosional features bear testimony to the active destruction of the upper platform. The promontories are undercut by as much as 2m, in places, by the notch at the head of the lower platform (Photo 12). Deep clefts in the rock masses are being opened up from below and their smooth walls indicate the effectiveness of abrasion by coastal sediments thrown about by breaking waves.

Some of the gullies which dissect the raised platform can be traced up to the base of deep gashes in the high cliffs. Here masses of.freshly fallen debris, large boulders together with a mixture of clay and stones, attest to the contribution of cliff erosion to the sediments on the sea shore. Furthermore the clayey nature of the material, and the deep gashes of rotten rock extending from the plateau surface at over 100m of elevation right down to sea-level, indicate the depth to which surface weathering has rotted the rock forming the plateau. It is but a small step to extend this observation to the shore platform, and suggest that the ravines dissecting it are former sites of deeply weathered rock, now etched out by marine processes. The lower rock platform, exposed to a width of 20-25m at low tides, is mantled by a thin veneer of flint shingle. The upper platform carries ancient beach material, in the form of iron-cemented sand containing rounded shingle.

Photo 12: Abrasion notch and overhang at the top of the low platform, South Hallsands.
This feature pre-dates the removal of beach sediment in the early twentieth century and is, therefore, related to a distant period of sea-level similar to that of today (visible only at low tide). Photo: Derek Mottershead.

Looking at the village ruins now, it is difficult to appreciate that the main street ran along between two lines of dwellings, one to seaward and one to the landward side. Of the buildings on the seaward side, the footings of an inn can still be seen on the seaward edge of the first promontory. In 1890 there was an extensive barrier of flint shingle almost up to the level of the raised platform and extending seaward from it. HWM lay some 30m seaward of the nearest buildings. The beach was wide enough for fishing boats to be drawn up (Photo 13a) and it effectively defended the village from storms and waves. The destruction of this beach led to the ruin of the village.

The change in the fortune of South Hallsands came with the decision of the Royal Navy to extend the dockyard at Devonport in Plymouth. Between 1897 and 1900, some 400 000 cubic metres of shingle were dredged from the seaward side of the barrier beach for the construction of concrete docks. Although the authorities believed that natural processes would replenish the beach, no replenishment occurred and the destructive effects of the dredging became apparent by the winter of 1900-01. The level of the beach in front of Hallsands village was lowered and the village directly exposed to the attack of storm waves. The original sea walls were undermined and sand and shingle were sucked out from the rock clefts behind them. This caused the collapse of houses which were built over the sediment-filled clefts rather than those over the rock platform. Dredging was terminated in 1902. Each winter storm created further damage and in 1904 a substantial concrete sea wall was completed, the fragmented remains of which can still be seen on the shore. Photographs taken at the time reveal the extent of the beach lowering and encroachment by the sea (Photo 13b). The wall held firm for a number of years until January 1917. A combination of high tides and a strong north-easterly onshore gale finally overwhelmed the village. Houses built on the bedrock were battered by high waves and tossed beach material, whilst those built over the chasms subsided into them as the supporting infill of sediment was washed out. By 1903, the beach level had already fallen by 3-4m causing the advance of HWM by 30m. Figure 12 shows comparative surveys of the profile of the beach made in 1903, 1923 and 1956 and clearly demonstrates the recession and lowering of the beach and the resultant shoreward advance of HWM.

The serious effect of these changes on the geography of the village is shown in Figure 13. The removal of the beach barrier, and the advance of HWM (ordinary tides) exposed clearly the outline of the raised rock platform. The location of the dwellings in relation to the substrate is also demonstrated. The dramatic changes in the appearance of South Hallsands is emphasised in Photos 13a-c.

In the light of information now available on the nature of Start Bay, and of modern understanding of coastal processes, there can be little doubt that the destruction of South Hallsands was an inevitable consequence of the removal of shingle. At the time it was assumed that natural processes would replenish the beach, but, since the gently shelving bed of Start Bay is mantled by sand, that could not happen. Even the large accumulation known as Skerries Bank (Figure 8) is composed of sand, not shingle. The position of Skerries Bank is betrayed by rough surface water offshore from Start Point and running across the face of the bay. Within Start Bay there is no source of comparable sediment with which the barrier shingle could be replaced.

Photo 13: South Hallsands.
(a) 1894, before dredging began, the village is protected by a wide expanse of shingle beach; (b) 1904, after the first damaging storms. Substantial depletion has already taken place and the sea has encroached right up to the village. The new sea walls built in 1903-04 are evident; (c) by 1980 the seaward row of houses has completely disappeared, and fragments remain of the landward row. Some of these are undercut by canyons etched out by the sea. Photos: (a) and (b) Cookworthy Museum, Kingsbridge; (c) Derek Mottershead.

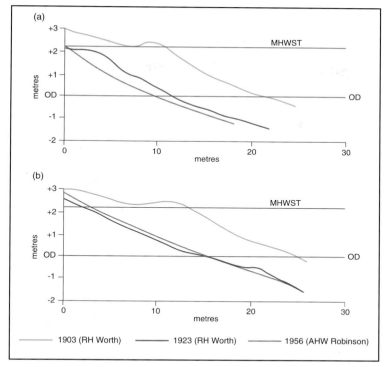

(a)

MHWST

OD

metres

(b)

MHWST

OD

metres

——— 1903 (RH Worth)   ——— 1923 (RH Worth)   ——— 1956 (AHW Robinson)

Figure 12: Beach profiles 1903, 1923 and 1956 at South Hallsands showing the depletion of the beach.

The bulk of changes to the profile had been completed by 1923. Not only was the beach surface lowered, but at high water the edge of the sea was over 10m closer to the village. Note that considerable depletion had already taken place prior to 1903. See Figure 13 for location of profiles. After: Robinson, 1961.

The former beach at Hallsands was emplaced under conditions of the past and was, like Slapton Sands, a fossil or relict form. Once removed artificially, it could not be replaced by natural processes under present conditions. The events at South Hallsands teach us a number of important lessons about coastal processes.

i   Beach sediment is not necessarily of contemporary origin. The presence of a beach does not necessarily indicate a contemporary supply of beach material.

ii An inter-tidal shore platform, currently washed by the sea, is not necessarily a contemporary feature. The low rock platform at Hallsands only became exposed to the sea after the removal of the overlying beach. It is not conceivable that such a feature planed across hard schist has been formed by wave action during the past 80 years. Its origin therefore pre-dates the formation of the beach, and it indicates that sea-level stood at its present position for a significant length of time prior to the last glacial period.

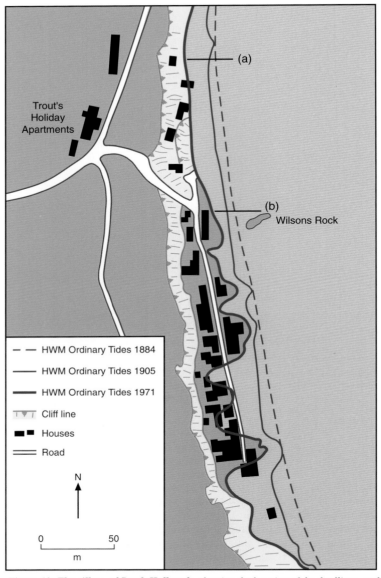

Figure 13: The village of South Hallsands, *showing the location of the dwellings, and the shoreward encroachment of HWM between 1884 and 1971. The two profiles shown in Figure 12 are indicated at (a) and (b).*

iii The non-renewal of the beach indicates that sediment does not circulate round Start Bay between Skerries Bank and the shore, and also that new material does not enter the Bay from outside.

iv The depletion of the beach and the subsequent disastrous effects of this action emphasise the need for a thorough understanding of

coastal processes before such large-scale works are undertaken.
v The timescale of the degradation of the beach indicates how
rapidly adjustments occur in the coastal systems. Large-scale
changes in the beach had to await the impact of high-energy
waves, such as occurred episodically under conditions of strong
easterly winds. From the onset of dredging it was three years
before beach levels began to fall, with further depletion evident
three years later. The final disaster took place 20 years after
dredging started, and 15 years after it ended. There is thus a
considerable lag between cause and effect in a system of this
scale.

The problems at Hallsands continue today. There is now concern for
the future of Hallsands Hotel and Mildmay cottages (SX 818388),
constructed at the clifftop at North Hallsands to replace dwellings lost
at South Hallsands, and which are now becoming threatened by cliff
erosion. The depletion of beach material has left the base of the cliffs
vulnerable to wave attack, especially along deeply-weathered faults
and fractures in the rock mass of which they are composed.

Access and safety

Slapton Sands can be accessed throughout their length, with car
parking available at both ends and by the war memorial. Unless the
sea is calm, particular care should be taken at the water's edge. There
is a footpath around the lower section of Slapton Ley: on the
landward side it can be accessed from Slapton Bridge and from the
A379 at the bottom of Stokenham Valley, while on the seaward side
it runs parallel to the main road. The sediments within the Ley, of
course are not visible unless sample cores are taken. The seafront at
Torcross is freely accessible through the village.

Approach the ruined village of South Hallsands on foot by a track
from Trout's Holiday Apartments (SX 817385). **Great care must be
taken.** Access has been restricted in recent years because of further
marine erosion, and at the time of writing (summer 1996) is
forbidden. It is hoped access will be restored in the near future.

The remains of the village can be viewed from above on the South
West Coast Path, some 200m south from Trout's Holiday Apartments,
where the path enters a tunnel of trees. It can also be viewed, though
more distantly, from Start Point car park (SX 821376).

The nearest adequate parking is at North Hallsands by the South
West Coast Path, landward of the Hallsands Hotel (SX 817386).
Parking at South Hallsands itself is somewhat restricted.

The Cookworthy Museum, 108 Fore Street, Kingsbridge, Devon
TQ7 1AW, has instructive displays (good for a rainy day). Displays
of photos and other material may also be viewed at Trout's Holiday
Apartments and at Torcross on the alley wall beside 'Waterside' bed
and breakfast (SX 823422).

DAWLISH WARREN

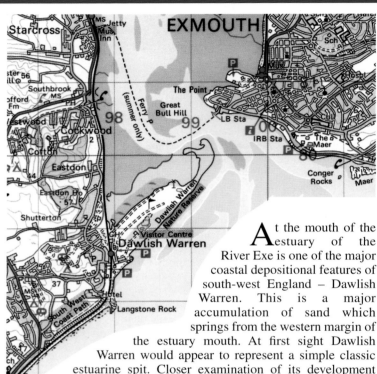

A t the mouth of the estuary of the River Exe is one of the major coastal depositional features of south-west England – Dawlish Warren. This is a major accumulation of sand which springs from the western margin of the estuary mouth. At first sight Dawlish Warren would appear to represent a simple classic estuarine spit. Closer examination of its development throughout historic time, however, reveals that it is not so simple, and raises a number of important issues regarding both spit development and coastal protection.

The spit extends northwards for a distance of some 2km from the Permian Breccia and Conglomerate bedrock terrain near Dawlish Warren station (SX 979787). Its orientation continues the trend of the cliff-line south of Langstone Rock (SX 979779), although the seaward face of the spit is set back some 33m from this line (Figure 14a). The planform of the spit exposed above HWM (which is at approximately +1.4m OD) shows it to be up to 500m broad over much of its length, narrowing rapidly towards the **distal** end. The distal point is strongly hooked, the accumulation of sand there demonstrating a series of recurves back into the estuary of the Exe. The unusual breadth of the spit above HWM is composed of several discrete elements, the principal components being two parallel ridges which demonstrate both qualitative and quantitative differences.

The seaward face of the spit, the Outer Warren, consists of a discontinuous line of sand hills some 5-6m in height and 25-50m wide backed by a tract of semi-fixed dunes of varying width. The tract extends now for approximately half the length of the spit, and is much reduced in relation to its former area. The second ridge, the Inner Warren, is an area of stabilised sand overlying a bed of clay of presumed estuarine origin. Its highest elevation is attained at the distal end, and it is lowest close to the mainland. The two ridges are separated by a depression known as Greenland Lake (SX 984790), formerly a tidal inlet, and now merely an area of marshy ground for much of the time. A further component of the exposed spit on its landward side is the strip of saltmarsh which has accumulated in its lee.

These four components, then, form the exposed part of the spit, as outlined by HWM. It is important to understand, however, that this represents only the highest part of a mass of sediments much larger in both plan and volume. Examination of the outline of the spit at low water reveals both its lateral extent and its relations with adjacent sediment bodies. The seaward face is fronted by an extent of beach from 100-300m in width. At its distal end it is connected to a large sand bank, Pole Sand, triangular in planform and extending for some 2km along the Exmouth shore, from which it is separated by the deep channel of the Exe. Within the mouth of the estuary, opposite The Point of Exmouth, is the large sandbank of Bull Hill Sand, separated from the distal end of the spit, Warren Point, by the low water channel of the Exe.

Behind the saltmarsh in the lee of Dawlish Warren there is a considerable expanse of mudflats. In this context, Dawlish Warren can be seen as just one component of the massive accumulation of sediments present at the mouth of a major river. Its significance as a landform is that its elevation exposes it above HWM. Its significance in relation to coastal processes is that it represents the cumulative effect of the variety of forces that are responsible for circulating sediments within the estuarine environment.

Further evidence of the context of the spit is available from seismic and borehole evidence. These reveal something of the internal structure of the spit and the surface on which it stands (Figure 14). A transect along the Warren reveals that a bedrock of Permian Breccia forms its foundation, with a surface sloping down from about zero OD near the railway line to -20m OD near Warren Point. This surface is cut by a series of deep channels meandering north-west to south-east to a depth of up to -40m OD. The breccia bedrock is partially overlain by gravels which infill some of the channels. The gravels outcrop at the surface at several points – Pole Sand, Shaggles Bank, Bull Hill Sand and Warren Point – at elevations of -1.3m to -1.6m OD. They are interpreted as river gravels, which are laid down both on the bedrock surface and in the previously cut bedrock channels. They are in turn overlain by clays and sands (Figure 14b), recent estuarine deposits culminating in the sands which form the bulk of the

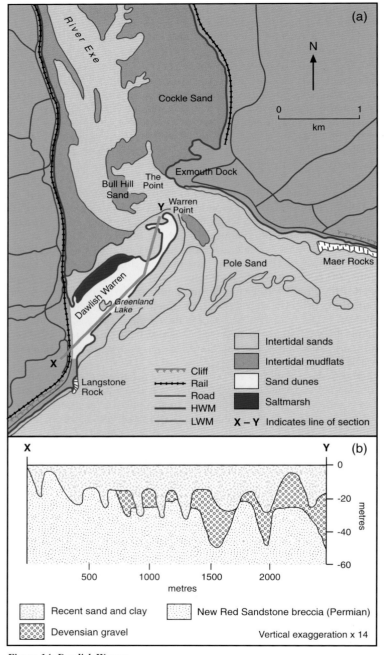

Figure 14: Dawlish Warren
*(a) its location in relation to features in the estuary of the River Exe, (b) profile along
the line X-Y showing its stratigraphic structure.*
After: Durrance, 1969.

46

exposed spit. The gravels may reasonably be interpreted as Devensian in age, which on stratigraphic grounds points to a more recent origin for the sand of the spits. In the context of the evolution of the lower Exe valley, then, Dawlish Warren can be seen as a comparatively young feature, occurring as the most recent in a sequence of sediments.

Within the topographic and stratigraphic framework outline above, it seems more likely that Dawlish Warren was emplaced by the Flandrian rise in sea-level, which terminated about 5000 years ago, sweeping sandy sediments into the mouth of the estuary. At this point it is appropriate to consider the source of the sand. It should be noted that the exposed surface of Dawlish Warren is composed exclusively of sand. It differs from the bars across the mouths of many rivers on this coastline which are composed of shingle (eg. the Teign, Axe, Otter, Sid). This implies that the source of the sediments of Dawlish Warren was qualitatively different from that forming the other bars.

Two possible sources suggest themselves (Figure 2). Kidson (1950) suggested that Dawlish Warren was nourished by rapid erosion of the cliffs to the west, to which it is linked. At the end of the Flandrian rise in sea-level it is inferred that cliff erosion would have been rapid and that an abundant supply of sediment would therefore have been available for transfer by **longshore drift** along the coast to Dawlish Warren. This is a reasonable hypothesis, but it does not explain why erosion of cliffs in similar rock elsewhere along the coast has provided only shingle sediment for bar construction in other estuaries. An alternative source may be sought in the deltaic sediments accumulating off the mouth of the Exe. It should be noted that the Exe drainage system is of an order of magnitude larger than any of the other rives along this coast, and accordingly, the volume of sediment it would have delivered to its outlet in the course of time would far outweigh that available from the smaller drainage systems. The rising sea-level of the Flandrian transgression would have provided a mechanism for driving the sediments onshore to form the spit. In the absence of published studies of the mineralogy of the sands of Dawlish Warren this alternative hypothesis must be regarded a realistic possibility. Furthermore, it is a 'once only' mechanism, and if true implies that sediment is no longer being supplied to the spit from this source. This, as we shall see, has implications for contemporary changes on Dawlish Warren.

Having established the relative impermanence of Dawlish Warren over the Quaternary timescale, we will now examine its development during historic time. Kidson (1950) examined the historical evidence of maps from 1787 onwards, and supplemented this with the evidence of more recent field surveys. The changes in the spit's outline are shown in Figure 15. It is clear that Dawlish Warren has undergone considerable change. More noticeable is the reduction in area of the feature as the seaward face has been eroded back by about 200m, at an average rate of 1.3m per year. Over the period 1949 to 1962 rates of loss along specific transect lines ran at several metres per year.

In contrast to the consistent retreat of the face of the spit, its behaviour at the distal end has been far more volatile. There have been phases when the spit was breached and the distal end became detached as an island sandbank. Each such phase was followed by regrowth and 'reconnection'. It is clear also that the position of the distal point has fluctuated to and fro by as much as 350m. The orientation of the spit indicates that it has grown from south-west to north-east. The predominant movement of beach material is in that direction towards Warren Point. Analysis of wind records suggests that twice as much wave energy is applied in this direction as in the opposite one. Sediment thus arriving at Warren Point may then be redistributed around it into the estuary by the tidal flood current or waves driven by south-easterly winds, or out towards Pole Sand by the tidal ebb current, according to the circumstances of the moment.

Breaching of the spit has been observed to occur when south-easterly gales, driving strong onshore waves, combine with high spring tides. In such conditions the sea has made inroads through the spit at its lowest and narrowest point, thereby detaching the end from the stem and forming an island. The fluctuations in the planform of the spit can therefore be seen as a response to sets of conflicting forces. Waves arriving obliquely to the shore from the south cause longshore drift and thereby spit extension and, in the absence of a renewed supply of sand, retreat of the dune face. In contrast large waves directly onshore cause overtopping and breaching of the spit. The distribution of sand around Warren Point involves a complex interplay of wind, waves and tidal currents. The history of breaching, regrowth and repair is a response to the variable interplay of these various sources of coastal energy.

The unusual double form of the spit described earlier deserves further comment. During windy weather sand can be observed blowing inland from the fresh and semi-fixed dunes of the Outer Warren. The prevailing direction of wind is from the south-west, and

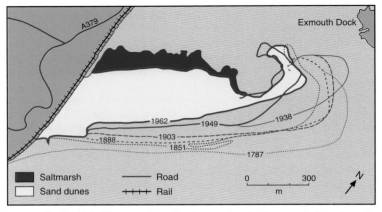

Figure 15: Dawlish Warren – historic changes in planform *as indicated by the position of HWM ordinary tides 1787-1962. After: Kidson, 1950.*

this would tend to drift the sand in a north-easterly direction. Accordingly, Kidson (1950) interprets the Inner Warren as an accumulation of windblown sand, noting that its greater elevation at the north-easterly end is consistent with the direction of the prevailing wind. The low ground between the two sand ridges was formerly occupied by a tidal inlet whose drainage would have swept it clear of accumulating sand. Only on the drier ground beyond would accumulation have been permitted, and this is now the site of the Inner Warren.

The high rate of evolution shown by Dawlish Warren is not due to an anomalously high rate of contemporary erosion, for erosion at the face of the spit has been taking place continuously for over 200 years. Some authors have suggested that the building of the railway in 1849 curtailed the erosion of the cliffs to the west, thereby cutting off the sediment supply from that source and initiating the retreat of the face of the spit. But that cannot be true, since the long-continued pattern of erosion suggests that the supply of sediment ceased long before that date. It suggests that only a finite volume of sediment was initially available for spit construction, and that once moulded into the form of a spit, erosion was then inevitable.

This substantial landform can therefore be seen as a very impermanent feature of the landscape. On the scale of Quaternary time it represents merely the most recent accumulation of sediment in the estuary of the River Exe. In historic time it has undergone considerable modification in response to contemporary coastal processes. Its origin must be sought in the abundant supply of sediment available at the end of the Flandrian transgression, its form having been moulded by the interplay of wind, waves and tides since that time.

Access

There is ample car parking by Dawlish Warren station, to the east of the rail line, which can be reached via the underpass beneath the railway (SX 581785). There are no safety problems other than the need always to be aware of the state of the tide. Access to the golf course is by written permission only, otherwise there is free access via footpaths throughout Dawlish Warren.

The area is both a Local Nature Reserve and a Site of Special Scientific Interest. Teignbridge District Council employs a warden service at Dawlish Warren (telephone 01626 863980) which offers assistance to teachers.

A good point from which to gain a panoramic view over Dawlish Warren is the summit of Langstone Rock (SX 979779) which is easily reached along the South West Coast Path along the rail line.

GLOSSARY

Algal bloom An excess growth of surface algae in a water body, which limits the penetration of sunlight to aquatic plants beneath, leading to their decomposition, oxygen depletion and the growth of bacterial populations.

Alluvium Sediment deposited by a river on a valley floor. More abundant downstream and commonly composed of sand and silt.

Berm A small ridge parallel to the water line on the upper part of a beach formed by the accumulation of sediment at a recent high water mark.

Blockfield A spread of large rock fragments mantling the surface of a slope. It is formed by the weathering of a rock outcrop either upslope, or in place.

Clasts Fragments of rock derived from a larger rock mass.

Denudational process Processes which contribute to the erosion of the land surface, incorporating both weathering and transportation.

Diatom Microsopic unicellular algae with cell walls formed from silica. Their skeletal remains, resembling delicate glass structures, accumulate at the bed of water bodies as the organism dies.

Distal Most distant from point of attachment, eg. spit to mainland.

Eutrophic Term used to describe a water body enriched by the influx of nutrients.

Fetch The distance of open water across which waves may be generated towards a coast.

Head (deposit) The sediment resulting from gelifluction. It commonly accumulates at the foot of a slope and is composed of locally derived material, unsorted, ill-bedded and containing angular stones.

Hypertrophic Term used to describe a water body highly enriched with nutrients.

Indurated Hardened by heat or pressure, or cemented by pore-filling minerals.

Longshore drift The lateral transport of sediment along the shore by waves arriving obliquely to the shoreline.

OD Ordnance Datum; mean sea-level at Newlyn, Cornwall. From this level all heights on British maps are calculated.

Periglacial Term describing a cold climate environment, in which frost and snow are dominant for a large part of the year.

Planform The shape of a feature in horizontal plan.

Schist A metamorphic rock comprising elongated crystals, and which has a tendency to split into thin layers.

Store A location in which materials in transit reside for a significant length of time.

Subaerial Term denoting denudation processes which operate at the land surface.

Tor An outcrop of bedrock left upstanding as a result of the removal of surrounding material by denudation processes.

Weathering Processes by which rock *in situ* is decomposed or disintegrated, and rendered available for transportation by other denudation processes.

BIBLIOGRAPHY

Brunsden, D. and Goudie, A. (1997) *Classic Landforms of the West Dorset Coast.* Geographical Association.

Durrance, E.M. (1969) 'The buried channels of the Exe' in *Geological Magazine,* 106, 174-89.

Hails, J.R. (1975) 'Some aspects of the Quaternary history of Start Bay, Devon' in *Field Studies,* 4.2, 207-22.

Heathwaite, L. (1993) 'Lake sedimentation' in Burt, T. (ed) *A Field Guide to the Geomorphology of the Slapton Region,* Field Studies Council/BGRG, 31-41.

Job, D. (1993) 'The Start Bay barrier beach system' in Burt, T. (ed) *A Field Guide to the Geomorphology of the Slapton Region,* Field Studies Council/BGRG, 47-56.

Kidson, C. (1950) 'Dawlish Warren: a study of the evolution of the sand spits across the mouth of the River Exe in Devon' in *Transactions of the Institute of British Geographers,* 16, 69-80.

Kidson, C. (1964) 'Dawlish Warren, Devon: Late stages in sand spit evolution' in *Proceedings of the Geologists Association,* 75, 167-84.

Morey, C.R. (1976) 'The natural history of Slapton Ley Nature Reserve IX: The morphology and history of the lake basins' in *Field Studies,* 4, 3, 353-68.

Morey, C.R. (1980) *The Origin and Development of a Coastal Lagoon System, Start Bay, South Devon,* unpublished M.Phil thesis, Council for National Academic Awards.

Mottershead, D.N. (1971) 'Coastal head deposits between Start Point and Hope Cove, Devon' in *Field Studies,* 3, 433-53.

Mottershead, D.N. (1982) 'Coastal spray weathering of bedrock in the supratidal zone at East Prawle, South Devon' in *Field Studies,* 5, 663-84.

Mottershead, D.N. (1997) 'A morphological study of greenschist weathering on dated coastal structures, South Devon, UK' in *Earth Surface Processes and Landforms,* 22(5), 491-506.

Mottershead, D.N. and Pye, K. (1994) 'Tafoni on coastal slopes, South Devon, UK' in *Earth Surface Processes and Landforms,* 19(6), 543-63.

Orme, A.R. (1960) 'The raised beaches and strandlines of South Devon' in *Field Studies,* 1.2, 109-30.

Robinson, A.H.W. (1961) 'The hydrography of Start Bay and its relationships to beach changes at Hallsands' in *Geographical Journal,* 127, 63-77.

Tanner, K.O.P. and Walsh, P.T. (1984) *Hallsands, A Pictorial History.* Sugden Design Associates, Truro.

Ussher, W.A.E. (1904) 'The geology of the country around Kingsbridge and Salcombe' in *Memoir of the Geological Survey of Great Britain.* London.

Worth, R.H. (1924) 'Hallsands and Start Bay. Part III' in *Reports and Transactions of the Devonshire Association for the Advancement of Science, Literature and Arts,* 55, 131-47.